Prompt Me Romance
Creative Writing Journal & Workbook

Prompt Me Series #5

By
Robin Woods

Epic Books Publishing

A boutique publishing company
www.epicbookspublishing.com

Lead Editor: Beth Braithwaite
Additional Editing: Brooke E. Wayne and Tamar Hela

Cover Design created on Canva by Robin Woods

All Photos taken by Robin Woods

Fonts: Century, Gothic Ultra

Summary: A wide variety of writing prompts for maximum inspiration.

Special Thanks to:
Brooke E. Wayne for the use of her Tanka poetry.
Tim, Ali, Jason, and Jenn for posing for pictures.
www.PerfectSunset.com for providing photo shoot locations.

[Creative Writing, Diary, Non-Fiction, Reference, Writing Workbook, Fiction Writing, Writing Journal]

ISBN-13: 978-1-941077-15-3
ISBN-10: 1-941077-15-3

Table of Contents

Introduction

As I was preparing for this workbook, I took a picture of the flowers my husband gave me for our seventeenth anniversary. Using those flowers seemed especially romantic, but at the same time, they reminded me of something a painter would capture. A masterwork that would take time and be a labor of love.

Writing can be a lot of work, and it often gets messy. But we sometimes even need help to get to the mess itself. When you begin to form your ideas, don't worry about grammar and punctuation. Simply getting the words down and experimenting is the most important part in the beginning. In order to become a better writer, you need to do three things:

1. Write often.

2. Read often.

3. Don't be afraid to make mistakes.

Embrace the mess, find your voice, and don't get discouraged. As Richard Bach once said:

"A professional writer is an amateur who didn't quit."

Think of these pages as your artist's studio. Experiment with color and style. You never know; you may start something that grows into a masterpiece.

How to Use This Book

There are a variety of different styles of prompts in this workbook to help you decide what works best for you. If one style or prompt doesn't work, move on. If it doesn't work for you today, it might tomorrow.

If the pronouns don't work for you, change the she to a he, or vice versa. Prompts are meant to be inspiration, not shackles.

Carry it around with you. Mess it up. Use different kinds of ink. Stick Post-Its all over it.

Now, go forth and write!

Picture Prompts

It has often been said that a picture is worth a thousand words—but that doesn't really help writers. However, a picture can inspire thousands of words.

Use the following photos to create a unique story.

Writing Challenge:

Use at least three of the five senses in each of your stories—or add an extra sense.

☐ Sight ☐ Taste ☐ Touch ☐ Smell ☐ Sound

Charts are in the reference section in the back.

Picture Prompt How To

We are visual beings, so let's use our graphic nature to find inspiration. Following this page, you will find fifteen photo prompts. Use each of them as a muse for a story. It can be super short or the beginnings of a novel.

This is a sample of what to do. When I see this picture, it makes me think of a tragic romance or a terrible breakup. So here is my story:

The doorbell jarred me from my Hallmark movie marathon. Grumbling, I tossed the blanket over the ottoman and set my peppermint tea aside. "Who dares disturb rainy day TV?" I muttered to myself as I shuffled to the door, my worn slippers making a Velcro sound with each step.

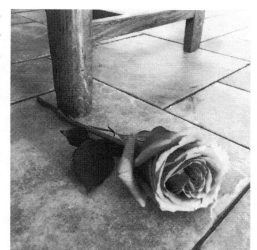

Confusion set in when I found a flower delivery boy on my stoop. He handed me a clipboard to sign that reeked of cigarettes and almost overpowered the flowers—at least two-dozen, blood red roses in a heavy, black vase.

I hefted it onto my hip and watched delivery boy run off into the rain, the fog half-enveloping him before he got to his car. Curious, I flicked the door shut with my foot and set the vase on the coffee table. "Hello, pretties. Now who sent you?"

Running my hands through the stems, I found the card stuck deep inside the arrangement. When I went to pluck it from the holder, I jerked my hand back. I'd managed to find the one and only thorn in the bunch, though I didn't see any others. Blood bubbled from my fingertip, and I rolled my eyes. Only I would bleed this much from something so lame. Before I bled out, I washed and bandaged my war wound. Thunder rattled my single-pane windows like I lived in a house next to an airport runway.

The roses caught my attention again. I grabbed my work gloves from the utility drawer before going for the card again. I loosed the envelope and stared at the written message inside.

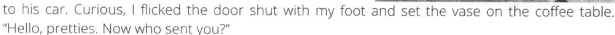

I've missed you every waking moment. Bound to you —W.

Breath left me as panic set in. I scrambled to the bedroom, heaving open the hidden panel in the floor and dragging out my go bag. I stripped off my pjs, jammed my legs in some jeans, then trotted through the house while zipping my pants—he'd found me.

With my bag in one hand and the car keys in the other, I had a horrible realization: it wasn't a thorn I'd pricked my finger on. I swayed on my feet, then the darkness devoured me.

1. Title: _____

2. Title: _____

3. Title: _____

4. Title: _____

5. Title: _____

6. Title: _____

7. Title: _____

8. Title: _____

9. Title: _____

10. Title: _____

11. Title: _____

12. Title: _____

13. Title: _____

14. Title: _____

15. Title: _____

Story Starters: First Person

Emotional Standpoint: Subjective
View: Limited
Pronoun Usage: I/we/us/me/my/mine/our/ours

Writing Challenge:

Limit the amount of times your character "felt" or "feels" something. Use active voice to help keep the reader in the experience.

First Person

16. It was simple—all I had to do was believe the lie.

17. I knew it sounded dark and obsessive, but I said it anyway. "I'm going to make her mine." It felt good to say and would be even better when it was true.

18. This was a mistake, but sometimes mistakes feel really good. Like when...

19. Finding what I needed, I pulled the books from the dusty library shelf. Only to find my eyes locked with the man on the other side of the shelf—*the very attractive man.*

20. The moment I felt the warmth of his hand, the power went out...

21. His smile was inviting, but something in my gut told me that his expression was a mask hiding.

22. As far as kisses go, a chorus of angels didn't appear in the sky, but my toes tingled.

23. Half embarrassed, I uttered, "I kinda thought you were falling for me. I didn't realize that you were being paid to follow me." But, I knew that there was...

24. Her eyes darted to mine for a split-second. *We were the only ones left.*

25. "Lucky for you, I like nerds." I grinned at him in all of his Clark Kent splendor. Take off those glasses and tousle his hair...

26. Shrugging, I answered, "I left a trail of breadcrumbs. What do you think happened?"

27. His forehead scrunched into a half-dozen lines as he examined me. Finally, he said, "I'm a good listener." I tried to swallow past the lump...

28. Crying in public wasn't on my 'to-do' list, so I darted into the stairwell before...

29. I grinned at him. "You like that? You'll love my fairy godmother. She likes to set things on fire."

30. Staring in the mirror, I chanted, "I'm not broken. I'm not broken."

31. "The last man who tried to control me ended up in an early grave," I spat. *Okay, he did end up in an early grave, but it had nothing to do with me.* I kept my brave face.

32. Her laugh made me feel about two inches tall. It was then that I noticed...

33. "Yeah, wanting to call me and actually calling me are two totally different things. Since both your hands are still attached to your body, I don't want to hear it." Then, I slammed the door shut, barely suppressing an eye roll.

Prompt # _____ Your Title: _____

34. Laughter rumbled deep inside me as I cooed, "You are only the beginning."

35. Not to be cliché, but his kiss literally made me weak in the knees. *Too bad there was no way it would work. Cause...wow.*

36. I giggled. "Did you just try to make me feel guilty for doing the right thing?"

37. When he opened the ring box, it contained a tiny, ruby pendant without the chain. I tried to hide my initial reaction, but...

38. My face was as hot as a three-alarm fire; he'd caught me looking.

39. "Pretty sure there isn't a single thing I like about you." I paused and thought for a moment. "Nope, not a single thing."

40. He sat there with a delicious look on his face. *I should have listened to my friends.*

41. We were wearing the same shirt. I couldn't decide if that was fate—or a really creepy coincidence.

42. Just one more kiss, then I would be able to say goodbye...even if it killed me.

43. In a sweeping motion, he was down on one knee with a small box nestled in his hand. When he grinned, my stomach did a flippity-flop, and my heart...

44. "You really are a good guy, aren't you?" I watched as he flinched on the word 'good.'

45. I gulped before forcing out the question through thin lips, "If you knew that being with someone would be their downfall, would you stay?"

46. That *thing* had its eyes set on the love of my life. It had exactly three seconds until...

47. Tears threatened to tumble down my cheeks. *Why did there have to be so many questions? Hadn't I proven myself?*

48. Wolves, barn owls, and even termites mate for life. I didn't understand why...

49. For the first time, I could clearly see the manipulation. *She was going to make a really evil ex.*

50. I pictured him dead. Then, badly wounded. Then, I tried not to think of him at all.

51. She was driving a wedge, but she didn't realize that I was onto her. Operation "Expose the She-Wolf" was commencing now.

52. If this is what he thought seduction was, he needed lessons...

53. Immediately, I stumbled to get away from the heated fight next to me; violence broke out. Just as an elbow struck my face, strong arms caught me, then sheltered me...

54. Groaning, I whined with humor, "Maybe it would be easier to stay single forever."

Prompt # _____ Your Title: _____

55. I rolled my eyes at myself. *An island full of single men, and I'm hiding in my room.*

56. Sharing a paddleboard seemed like a romantic idea, but it could possibly be the worst idea ever. We weren't in sync at all. Each time...

57. It was like living surrounded by barbed wire. As long as I stayed...

58. Tapping open the app, I was met with a picture of us last night and over a hundred impassioned comments. My heart picked up speed. The photo made it look like...

59. My eyes fluttered open, the taste of salt and something sweet on my lips...

60. When I went to take a sip of my new drink, a man quickly put his hand over the top of the glass. "Stop," he warned. "The bartender put something in it."

61. Cameras were everywhere; I couldn't help but wonder if he was watching...

62. Music throbbed in my ears as we danced to the rhythm pulsing through the open air at the festival. Losing myself, I twirled...

63. Giddy, I giggled until it sounded a little crazed. I couldn't stop myself...

64. Night air, warm and fragrant, seemed to wrap around us and beckon us forward as we walked...

65. Biting my lip, I didn't let the cowboy hat and smell of horse distract me...

66. Part of me wondered how he was going to react when he found out that I was an assassin too. But I shrugged off the thought and smiled over my drink.

67. I kept telling myself to breathe, but it was getting harder with each step...

68. Breaking up with someone on their birthday—especially when planned, seemed especially heinous.

69. It's like ripping off a Band-Aid; you just have to do it with commitment...

70. Glancing at her again, I couldn't help thinking she looked like my ex. *Except for her hair color and eyes. No, she didn't look like my ex. I just couldn't go there.*

71. My air tank was running low, and, if I didn't succeed, he would never know...

72. Despite hands gnarled with age, she gracefully sketched a picture of our future. The aged hands didn't match the fluid movements, then I realized it was really her...

73. His love felt like it was a supernova, until...

74. Our love wasn't tidy. In fact, everything had pretty much been a mess since the beginning, but it wasn't our fault—for real. We were healthy, but...

75. If our story had started in reverse, the beginning would've been much happier...

Prompt # _____ Your Title: _____

Prompt # _____ Your Title: _____

Prompt #_____ Your Title: _____

Story Starters: Third Person

Third Person Limited
Emotional Standpoint: Objective
View: Limited
Pronoun Usage: he/she/it/him/his/her/they/their

Third Person Omniscient
Emotional Standpoint: Objective
View: Unlimited
Pronoun Usage: he/she/it/him/his/her/they/their

Deep Third Person
Emotional Standpoint: Subjective
View: Limited
Pronoun Usage: he/she/it/him/his/her/they/their

Writing Challenge:

Vary your language, especially your sentence openings. I.e. Not every sentence should begin with "The" or "Then."

Third Person

76. If the kiss lasted much longer, she wouldn't be able to stop herself from tazing him.

77. Her eyes were shrewd as she watched the room. It didn't escape him. He knew she was security of some sort—*the attractive kind whom no one would suspect of being lethal.*

78. He was used to routine—it was comforting to him. And she turned his world into chaos.

79. Wind whipped her hair wildly into her face, so at first, she didn't see him drop to a knee in front of her.

80. Blinking back tears, she comprehended that he wasn't like the others.

81. A chill crept up his spine, and at that moment, he knew she was standing behind him. It was like his body was a finely honed instrument made to sense her presence.

82. Ignorant bliss and knowing the whole truth were universes apart in this case…

83. Worry creased her brow. "He warned me that he would hurt me. I didn't believe him." She then realized that he'd excused his bad behavior ahead of time.

84. In the past, toxic behavior had broken him. He vowed to avoid all women who…

85. Death had only been part of it. Her husband had chosen to haunt her—literally. Every night at 11:00 PM, he appeared in the hall and…

86. Growing up next door to him was intimidating. But she wouldn't let their past…

87. He kept texting her to make sure that she was all right. He didn't realize that every time he did that he was hitting the reset button on her pain.

88. The phone screen remained dark; my "excuse to leave" text was super late…

89. Library types had always been particularly attractive to him. Maybe it was the reserved nature, or maybe it was their ability to think deeply. He knew with this one…

90. "This is no time for romance," she argued, but all she could think about were his lips.

91. Glitter shimmered and fell from her hair with each movement like soft falling snow on a still evening…

92. Meeting in a cemetery wasn't the only odd beginning…

93. Flexing his toe, he poked it through the hole in the top of his shoe. A long sigh escaped him, one that seemed to come from his very soul. He felt like an old shoe…

94. She wasn't sure what cologne he was wearing, but it should have been named "Girl Repellant."

Prompt # _____ Your Title: _____

95. Grinning like an idiot, he quipped, "That sounds like a threat."

96. Deep down, he knew something was missing. When he was around her, this twinkle of hope seemed to gather at the innermost part of his chest. But when...

97. Crickets sang in the lonely night, making the sticky air seem even more smothering...

98. The ground was half-frozen, making him wonder if it was any less treacherous than trying to reach her...

99. "Do you want to kiss me or kill me? You need to decide," he urged.

100. He stared at the list of "50 Date Ideas" in desperation. "Go skating" or "play laser tag" weren't going to cut it. Besides, his aversion to...

101. The power surged, and then went out entirely; it was then she slid her hand into his...

102. Flailing her hands in exasperation, she said, "He's my best friend. You have no reason to be jealous. We literally shared a crib when we were babies."

103. At those words, he turned on his heel and shouted, "There's a reason you're single!"

104. Swallowing past the lump in her throat, she tried to remain calm. It all made sense—the money, cars, power, clothes—he worked for the mob.

105. Raising an eyebrow, she grinned, "Admit it. You were hitting on me."

106. For a long moment, he stood there debating. He seemed to sway on his feet, the weight of his decision crushing. "It would be easier to quit," he murmured under his breath.

107. "What's your biggest weakness?" she asked, goading him.

108. Déjà vu pricked at the waitress until she stopped and asked, "Is your name Helen?" By the way the woman blinked before answering, she knew the woman was about to lie.

109. He chuckled, "Is there a secret handshake or something?"

110. The dream was so real. Last night he'd dreamt that they were married. White picket fence and all. He'd felt genuine happiness for the first time in two years. But, he...

111. A poker face was *not* her strongest trait—telling cringe-worthy truth was.

112. Everything ached. Every muscle. Every bone. Even her brain hurt, and he didn't seem to have any ill effects at all. She would have to hate him later.

113. Petting his cat, it stretched and yowled happily. At least she'd won it over...

114. Easing into the hot bath was perfection. She'd been dreaming of it all day, except there was an absence of wine, chocolate, and someone even hotter massaging her feet.

115. When she laughed it was light and musical, but her eyes conveyed something different.

Prompt # _____ Your Title: _____

116. He expected her to give up her career? *The arrogance*, she thought.

117. Cats scattered as she trekked up the steep staircase. Each step groaned and crackled in such an alarming amount that she sent a prayer of thanks when she reached the top.

118. "You're a vegan?" she asked. Judging from his truck, she'd thought he was 100% beef.

119. For the fifth time, he patted his pocket absently as if he needed reassurance that a treasure was safely tucked inside...

120. Something much more sinister was afoot inside the old house. He feared...

121. Breath escaped in a long, steady stream; she watched as the bubbles rose to the surface of the water. She'd have thought them beautiful if she wasn't about to die...

122. A shadow passed in front of her, but she hadn't seen what was attached to said shadow.

123. Picnics in the park were supposed to be romantic. But between the persistent ants, dive-bombing birds, and swarm mosquitos, they felt as if they were...

124. Bumping between people like a pinball, she searched for an escape from the...

125. "Next time I surprise you with dinner, I'll call first," he uttered as he kept pressure on his head wound.

126. Droplets pelted them as they ran past the high-rise, but it wasn't rain...

127. He added fresh rosemary and stirred the dish slowly while surreptitiously taking a peek at her. She sat cross-legged on his couch with his photo album resting...

128. Whining wasn't going to solve the problem, he realized—*make it quick like a Band-Aid.*

129. The worry-line between his eyes deepened as he thought. When he finally met her eyes, she knew he'd made a decision, and she knew...

130. Breaking up had been so much easier than he'd thought. Then he found the dead rat.

131. Rejected at first, she became aware that his words didn't match his body language. He still wanted her—badly.

132. Meanwhile, he sat rigid on the bench, as if moving caused him pain.

133. Spots of light began to bleed through the cloud cover. Slow at first, then the heavens seemed to reveal itself all at once in a spectacular show of grandeur.

134. She pulled the reigns to the right and clicked her tongue, but it made no...

135. "I work better alone," he growled. But he knew he needed her help. He also knew he was compromised because he was attracted to her. She was innocent and had no idea what that did to him.

Prompt # _____ Your Title: _____

Prompt # _____ Your Title: _____

Prompt # _____ *Your Title:* _____

Use These Phrases

Writing Challenge:

Writers often forget to incorporate the sense of smell into their writings. Try to use this sense in an offbeat way. Charts are in the back to help with inspiration.

136. Choose and use at least six of these ten phrases:

charming jingle of laughter	clap of angry thunder
bite of cold wind	glow of firelight
smell of damp pavement	desire unfurled inside
lashes fluttered in surprise	odd feeling of security
embarrassment warmed her cheeks	delicious fragrance of baked goods

137. Choose and use at least seven of these ten phrases:

dashed through the crowd	peppermint infused
elusive feeling slinked away	lush fur tickled
lingering smell of pine	confessions in the velvet darkness
slave to his stomach	crunch of broken glass
slanderous friend turned enemy	unabashedly bold

138. Choose and use at least eight of these ten phrases:

liquid warmth of satisfaction	glimmered indistinctly
sunniest disposition	quiet as crunching on corn nuts
mixture of awe	a blush high on her cheeks
toe-curling fear	hair like spun gold
shivered against the fog	neither courage nor self-respect

139. Choose and use at least nine of these ten phrases:

groped in the midnight air	scarlet dripping
folded quietly in his thoughts	slushed along the mushy trail
reveling in her presence	red mouth yawning daintily
zing of lemon	amber glow through the window
raw, animal magnetism	sprang to his feet

140. Choose and use at least nine of these ten phrases:

intense earnestness	musical cadence of her voice
sweetness of honey	smell of warm rain on hot pavement
wearing a hungry look	rattling bones
perfumed air drifted	sweltering throng of people
mushroomed over the sides	indifferent expression

Prompt # _____ Your Title: _____

Choose a Path

Writing Challenge:

Use at least three of the five senses in each of your stories.

☐ Sight ☐ Sound ☐ Smell ☐ Taste ☐ Touch

If your story has fantasy elements, you can always add a sixth sense.

141. **She opened the door expectantly, then…**

- ☐ strolled back inside, assuming he would follow.
- ☐ stumbled backwards, trying to escape the men invading her home.
- ☐ gasped at the bouquets of flowers on her stoop.
- ☐ when no one was there, wondered if he was watching.
- ☐ snatched the envelope from the investigator's hands.

142. Wandering leisurely down the avenue, he...

- ☐ smiled at the pageantry of the festival and the girl holding his hand.
- ☐ wondered if it was too soon to call her.
- ☐ spotted the restaurant he planned to use as a venue for his proposal.
- ☐ broke into a sprint when he witnessed her being dragged into a van.
- ☐ stopped in his tracks when his ex stepped out of a store.

143. At the sound of the buzzer,...

- ☐ he dropped to a knee in front of the jumbo cam at the game.
- ☐ she squealed in excitement; her wait was over.
- ☐ her best friend dove into the pool with singular focus.
- ☐ birds took flight in a fantastical roar.
- ☐ it was time to make a choice—a permanent one.

144. A pause in the sound...

- ☐ announced the coming of troops in their fancy dress uniforms.
- ☐ made her glance up to see what was wrong, then their eyes met.
- ☐ gave them a break to see who had departed.
- ☐ had the deejay scrambling to fix the problem.
- ☐ halted their already awkward conversation.

145. First day...

- ☐ of the new job shouldn't be ruined by an overly, attractive boss.
- ☐ of summer, and she was already packed and in flip-flops.
- ☐ in lock-up was at an end. If only he could tell her why.
- ☐ after the breakup had him reeling—he felt both free and angry.
- ☐ of the solstice, and they were already fighting.

_____

_____

_____

_____

_____

_____

_____

_____

_____

_____

_____

_____

_____

_____

_____

_____

_____

146. Relief washed over…

- ☐   him when she finally said, "Yes," with a tremulous voice.
- ☐   the minister when the bride stopped her sobbing hiccups.
- ☐   her when she realized she still had a credit card in her pocket.
- ☐   the masked crowd when the pops turned out to be balloons.
- ☐   her when the unlocked door swung open to reveal a trail of rose petals.

Dialogue Prompts

A few tips before we start:

- ☐ Avoid using the characters' names too much in dialogue.
- ☐ Make sure not all of your characters sound the same.
- ☐ Try not to have characters parrot or repeat the previous sentence.

Writing Challenge:

Use as few adverbs as possible.

- ☐ Generally, people don't speak in complete sentences. Use some fragments.
- ☐ Play with dialect and the way your characters use contractions.
- ☐ Restarts, stumbles, and stutters can improve emotional scenes.

147. "I don't negotiate with terrorists."

    "What are you talking about? I'm your boyfriend, not a terrorist."

148. "Loving me is a death sentence."

"If you haven't noticed, I'm not very smart."

149. "Real people don't have abs like that."

"It's prosthetics and Photoshop, I assure you."

150. "If you run, I'll chase you."

"Maybe I want to be caught."

151. "She threatened to kill herself if I left."

   "What did you do?"

   "I handed her a knife."

152. "You are such a narcissist!"

"Just because I don't want to die? I don't see that in the job description."

153. "I wanted you back."

"So, kidnapping was your go-to?"

154. "You've been missing for five years."

    "Is that a problem?"

More dialogue prompts...

155. "Hide me."

    "What? Why?"

    "My blind date from last night is behind you."

156. "I guess I'm naturally contrary."

    "If contrary was a handgun, you'd be a nuclear bomb."

157. "When I was a kid, I was afraid of monsters under the bed."

    "And now?"

    "Those aren't the type of monsters I should've feared."

158. "Picking you wasn't a willy-nilly decision."

    "Then, I'm honored."

    "You should be, I pulled your name out of that hat like a boss."

159. "Forgive my tardiness, I didn't want to come."

    "Better late than dead I always say."

    "That's...reassuring."

160. "It's not my fault."

    "I got fired."

    "That might be my fault."

Prompt # _____ Your Title: _____

Fill in the Blank: 49 Possibilities

Writing Challenge:

Try writing from a different point of view. For added challenge, write the same scene twice from two different perspectives.

161. If I _____ then I will ___.

Blank One	Blank Two
go with him	make her leave me
ask him out	betray my kingdom
marry him	be an object of jealousy
tell her the truth	live happily ever after
tell the press	give up my career
reveal I'm poor	show her the real world
reveal I'm rich	be setting myself up for rejection

162. He traveled _____ and found ___.

Blank One	Blank Two
to a distant land	that the assassin he was hunting was beautiful
back in time	that he'd met his new boss before
to the next city	himself in chains
to a desert colony	a pit of snakes. *It had to be snakes.*
to the underworld	his ex with the new bimbo
to the nearest oasis	he was attracted to his enemy
by elevator to the meeting	that his dreams really could come true.

163. **When the car ___, she realized ___.**

Blank One	Blank Two
sputtered to a stop	his intentions and burst into laughter
swerved in front of her	he wanted her to follow
hit a pedestrian	she had no food or water
turned out to be a gift for her	the gas gage was broken
revved its engine	he was toying with her
window rolled down	her purse was in the other car
turned out to be two motorcycles	she would destroy him

164. His romantic gesture __ when he __.

Blank One	Blank Two
fell flat in an instant	cued the full orchestra to start playing
delighted her	arrived on a horse
was swoon worthy	failed to call her for four days
made her question his motives	lost his balance and fell in the pool
was more than epic	kept smiling at his ex
embarrassed her	put his coat on the puddle
was storybook perfect	serenaded her in front of her parents

The Romance of It

Writing Challenge:

Give your character a secret that influences all of his or her decisions.

The Romance Arc

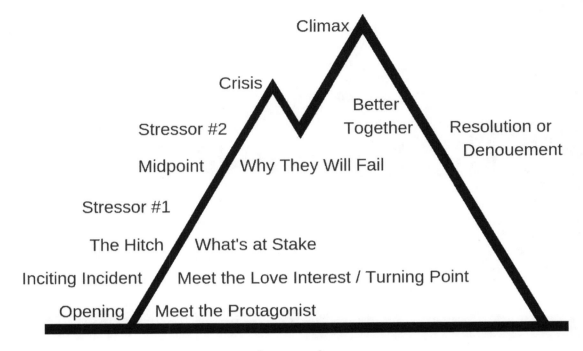

Climax

Crisis

Better
Together

Stressor #2

Resolution or
Denouement

Midpoint   Why They Will Fail

Stressor #1

The Hitch   What's at Stake

Inciting Incident   Meet the Love Interest / Turning Point

Opening   Meet the Protagonist

Standard Romance
Story Arc

Notes:

165. Fill-in the Romance Story Chart.

Act One	
Opening Who is the protagonist?	
Inciting Incident How does the protagonist meet the love interest?	
Why do they need to spend time together?	
The Hitch What conflict threatens the romance?	
Act Two	
What kind of sexual tension is happening?	
Midpoint How are the protagonist's goals or desires conflicting with the relationship?	
Crisis How are the goals or desires put in front of the relationship?	
Act Three	
Climax What does the protagonist give up in order to stay in the relationship?	
Resolution How has the protagonist become whole?	

Biology & the Bases—Stages of Intimacy

There have been many books written on human behavior and intimacy. One concept found in many of these books is the 12 Stages of Intimacy. This scientific concept can also be a great outline for the course of a relationship. Each time your love interests meet, you can play with which number they get to. Keep the tension and never skip a step. In fact, it will build tension if you backtrack each time. I have also included the classic "bases" baseball analogy.

12 Stages of Intimacy

1. Eye to body. The initial spark of interest.

2. Eye to eye. Decision time—real interest or walk away?

3. Voice to voice. Building blocks in the attraction. Getting to know one another.

4. Hand to hand. This can be an accidental brush of the fingers or conscious touching.

5. Hand to shoulder. Much more intimate

6. Hand to waist. Increasing intimacy, not allowed by a casual stranger.

7. Face to face. (FIRST BASE) ←Kissing!

8. Hand to head. We don't usually let just anyone touch our faces. Savor this.

9. Hand to body. (SECOND BASE) ← Above the waist, also known as petting.

Note: Young Adult literature usually stops here. Anything beyond this is usually NA, Adult, or Erotica.

10. Mouth to body. At this point, it is very hard to stop. Hormones have been released.

11. Touching below the waist. (THIRD BASE) ←Hot and heavy, even harder to stop.

12. Consummation. (HOME RUN) ←All the way.

Morris, D. (1971). *Intimate Behaviour: A Zoologist's Classic Study of Human Intimacy.*

166. Write a scene using two of the 12 Stages of Intimacy.

Anatomy of a Hot Kiss

Hot kisses are an essential part of almost any romance story. Here are a few tips.

A. Set the stage
B. Build anticipation
C. Focus on the emotion of the scene (nothing gratuitous needed)
D. Leave your reader wanting more

Setting the stage

"Are you well?" he asked as he walked in, concern creeping onto his face.

I didn't answer, but held out my arms, bidding him to come to me. He stood before me and placed his hands in mine, looking down at them. His hands were perfect, like everything else about him. I ran my thumbs over his knuckles and pulled him a half-step closer. He edged forward, and I cupped his face.

Build Anticipation

I traced his cheekbones and brows, then his perfectly-chiseled nose. We stood nose-to-nose with the aid of the step, his blue eyes piercing and full of questions.

Running my right thumb gently over his lips, I finally drew his mouth to mine for the first time.

Use more than just sight.

He took in a startled breath at the last moment, clearly not expecting me to actually kiss him. His lips were soft and firm and tasted sweet. My mouth moved slowly as I leaned into him. His hands found my hips as my arms encircled his neck. I pulled him against me, feeling the hard planes of his chest press against the softness of mine.

Escalate the intensity

My kisses became more feverish, and I brushed the tip of my tongue across his top lip. They parted as he let out a gasp. I ran my fingers through his hair and grabbed on hard, desperation driving me. His hands ran upwards, one accidentally catching the hem at the bottom of my shirt. I sucked in a shaky breath, feeling his hand on the bare skin of my lower back.

Emotion of the moment

I felt like I had an ocean raging inside me, undulating and pulling at my very core—waves of emotion colliding and collapsing on one another. Our breathing was ragged and fast. He pulled me closer, his arms enveloping me, my feet barely on the ground.

The barriers I'd so carefully built were chaotically crashing in on me.

Tears welled up in my eyes as I pulled myself away. He looked at me in an awe-struck daze, as a warm tear tumbled down my cheek.

He straightened up slightly and held my face between his hands, wiping the next tear tenderly away with his thumb. "I love you. I always have, and I always will."

Leave them wanting more

A sob escaped my lips. "D-don't say that. Please," I whimpered, breaking his gaze. It was obvious he loved me, but hearing him say it aloud for the first time—*now*—I'd been so careful to keep him at a distance. Pushing past him, I ran from the room.

Excerpt from The Sacrifice a Paranormal Romance by Robin Woods

167. Write a kissing scene involving a first—or last kiss.

Choose Your Genre

Genre	Historical	Contemporary	Paranormal	Steampunk
Hero	Lawyer	Billionaire	Mechanic	Vampire
Heroine	Thief	Teacher	Werewolf	Reporter

Situation	First meeting	First kiss	First fight	First date

168. Pick a genre and a situation. Write a scene using all five senses.

Genre	Comedy	Fantasy	Thriller	Sci-Fi
Hero	Banker	Mundane	Spy	Alien
Heroine	Detective	Fae	Uber driver	Pilot

Situation	First meeting	First kiss	First fight	First date

169. Pick a genre and a situation. Write a scene using all five senses.

_____

_____

_____

_____

_____

_____

_____

_____

_____

_____

_____

_____

_____

_____

_____

_____

Love Languages

People love in different ways, but for the majority of people, their needs are met in five different areas. In general, we have one primary area and a strong second. What are your characters love languages? How do they express them? How do they react when their needs are not met? How can this cause conflict? Use this to build real characters and complexity.

Love Languages

Acts of Service

Doing things for your partner—especially the mundane.
E.g. Changing a diaper, making the bed, taking out the trash, setting the table, walking the dog, or doing other small jobs. Also, extras like making coffee and putting it on the nightstand as your partner wakes up. It is the thoughtfulness that counts.

Quality Time

Having your partner's undivided attention.
E.g. Making eye contact, putting away electronics, attentive listening, special date nights, one-on-one time, etc.

Words of Affirmation

Verbal acknowledgment of care.
E.g. Compliments, words of encouragement, gratitude, empathy, respect, admiration, poetry, handwritten notes, etc.

Receiving Gifts

"Visual symbols of love"
Meaningful gifts to show appreciation.
(Not necessarily materialistic--they can be made, found, or bought—even from the dollar store)
E.g. love note, flowers, chocolates, etc.
It is the meaningfulness that counts.

Physical Touch

Physical contact to express affection.
E.g. Snuggling, holding hands, kissing, hugging, back rubs, sex, etc.
Having non-sexual affection is very important to this person.

Reference: Gary Chapman (1995). *The Five Love Languages: How to Express Heartfelt Commitment to Your Mate.* Northfield Publishing. ISBN 1881273156.

170. Your characters have conflicting love languages. Write a scene with some comedy.

Woo with Flowers

171. Create a bouquet of flowers using the chart on the next page. Write a scene where the flowers add depth to the action.

The Meaning of Flowers

The following meanings and symbolism have been gathered over the years and compiled from older texts, especially from the Victorian Era. Some of the meanings have changed in recent years (I blame the florists), but in the literary world, the older meanings still have merit. Note: Some meanings vary with the color and in the context in which it is given.

Almond—Indiscretion, carelessness
Amaryllis—Immortality, unfading love
Apple Blossoms— Preference
Azalea—Temperance
Bluebell—Constancy
Camellia—Red - Loveliness; White - Excellence
Carnation—Pink - A woman's love; Red - Alas my poor heart
　　　　　　　Striped - Refusal; Yellow - Disdain
Chrysanthemum—Red - Love; Yellow - Slighted love; White - Truth
Columbine—Folly
Daffodil—Regard
Daisy—Innocence, I will think on it
Fern—Fascination
Gladiolus—Strength of character
Hawthorne—Hope
Heather—Solitude
Ice Plant—Your looks freeze me
Ivy—Friendship, fidelity, faithfulness
Jasmine—Grace, elegance
Lavender—Purity, calmness, caution (and sometimes, distrust)
Lilac—Wisdom, first emotions of love
Lily—Sweetness, purity
Magnolia—Dignity, nobility
Mint—Virtue, moral excellence
Mistletoe—I surmount all difficulties
Myrtle—Power, sincerity, love
Narcissus—Egotism
Rose—Red - Love; White - Purity; Burgundy - beauty
　　　　Yellow - Decrease of love, infidelity
Rosemary—Remembrance, faithfulness
Rue—Regret, disdain
Sunflower—Confidence, courage, pride (and sometimes haughtiness)
Tulip—Undying passionate love
Wisteria—Success, I cling to you

That's Classic

Writing Challenge:

Combine three different character archetypes into a single character for a unique
blend of traits. A chart is in the back to help.

Plots to "Steal"

Use pieces of these famous plots to help formulate something with a fresh twist or a complete reimagining. After all, *The Lion King* is three parts *Hamlet*. You can do it too. Mix two together or change the gender to make it fresh.

172. *Romeo & Juliet* (Shakespeare): Children from rivaling families fall in love and cause tensions to escalate. Will their love unite the warring families? Or save them?

173. *Taming of the Shrew* (Shakespeare): A declared forever-bachelor from out of town takes a bet to woo the local man-hater. Will they fall in love before she finds out it was a setup? Will her presence in his life make the man who loves the single life love relationships?

174. *Twelfth Night* (Shakespeare): A young, highborn woman is shipwrecked and swept ashore in a foreign land. Thinking her brother drowned, she assumes his identity and goes into town to find work. Since she is disguised as a man, the woman her new boss is in love with falls for her, instead of the boss. Meanwhile, she falls in love with her boss. Will any of them find love? Will the fact that she pretended to be her brother ruin everything?

175. *Othello* (Shakespeare): A man of importance is desperately in love with his wife until a jealous coworker casts seeds of doubt and eventually frames the wife as a cheater. Will the husband find out in time? Or will he make a terrible mistake ending in death?

176. *The Scarlet Letter* (Hawthorne): Thinking her husband dead, a beautiful woman finds love in the arms of another man. When she conceives a child, she keeps the identity of her lover a secret to protect his life from a community who would kill him for having an affair with a married woman. Plot twist, her husband didn't die—he shows up in town after the child is born and vows to make the man she had the affair with pay.

177. *The Great Gatsby* (Fitzgerald): A poor, yet handsome, soldier falls in love with a rich girl. Realizing he doesn't have the money to marry her, he leaves to seek his fortune, resorting to trafficking illegal goods to do it. When he returns, the girl is married and in an unhealthy relationship. Can he reclaim the past?

178. *Emma* (Austen): After a new girl moves to town, the heroine befriends her and decides to play matchmaker. After shoving her new friend towards a suitor, he does falls in love, but not with the friend, but rather the heroine. Rejected and humiliated, the friend quickly falls for the neighbor of the heroine. The only problem is, once the friend announces her new found love, the heroine realizes that she, too, is in love with the boy next door. Will the heroine dash her friend's dreams and steal the boy? Does the boy next door feel the same way? How did matchmaking go so wrong?

179. *Pygmalion* (Shaw): A man bets his colleague that he can improve a poor woman's life by teaching her to behave like someone from the upper class. But once he gets to know her, can his heart withstand her pure heart? If she find out about the bet, can she ever trust him? Will pride ruin everything? [Mentor/Protégé]

Romance Trope Bingo

		Free Space		

Instructions: 1. Photocopy this blank form for the number of players (or draw on paper). 2. Have each player write one favorite trope from the next page into each box. 3. Photocopy the list of tropes on the next page and cut out each of the 65 tropes separately. 4. Draw numbers until everyone has a bingo. 5. Prizes optional.

Classic Trope Bingo

180. There are many classic tropes prevalent in romance. Have some fun mixing and matching them—or play a round of bingo with some friends. Challenge each other to have to use all four of their one-line bingo wins in their story.

1. Accidental Pregnancy	34. Lost Heir
2. Adversaries	35. Love Triangle
3. Allies Against a Common Enemy	36. Mail Order Bride
4. Alpha Hero	37. Matchmaker
5. Amnesia	38. Mentor and Protégé
6. Arranged Marriage	39. Military Life
7. Athlete	40. Nanny and the Parent
8. Bachelor Playboy	41. Office Romance
9. Bad Boy and the Good Girl	42. On the Rocks
10. Beauty and the Beast	43. Opposites Attract
11. Best Friend's Sibling	44. Orphan
12. Betrayal	45. Prodigal Son
13. Billionaire	46. PTSD
14. Blackmail	47. Quest
15. Boy Next Door	48. Rags to Riches
16. Celebrity and the Commoner	49. Redemption
17. Cougar	50. Reunion
18. Cyrano	51. Revenge
19. Damsel in Distress	52. Royalty
20. Dark Secret	53. Runaway Bride
21. Enemies to Lovers	54. Secret Baby
22. Fairytale	55. Secret Identity
23. Fake Engagement	56. Shunned by Society
24. Fear of Commitment	57. Social Class Difference
25. Fish Out of Water	58. Stranded
26. Fling	59. The Ex
27. Forbidden Love	60. Time Travel
28. Friends to Lovers	61. Transformation
29. Green Card	62. Unrequited Love
30. Hostage	63. Virgin
31. Inheritance	64. Wager
32. Jilted Lover	65. Widow
33. Kidnapped	

Swoon Worthy Lines

My bounty is as deep as the sea,
My love as deep; the more I give to thee,
The more I have, for both are infinite.
—**William Shakespeare**

My love is selfish. I cannot breathe without you. —John Keats

You were made perfectly to be loved - and surely I have loved you, in the idea of you, my whole life long. —Elizabeth Barrett Browning

I love thee, I love but thee;
with a love that shall not die;
till the sun grows cold
and the stars grow old.
—**William Shakespeare**

You are always new, the last of your kisses was ever the sweetest. …give up your whole heart to me whose whole existence hangs upon you. You could not step or move an eyelid but it would shoot to my heart – I am greedy of you – Do not think of any thing but me. —John Keats

Eternity was in our lips and eyes. —**William Shakespeare**

I pour out my thoughts to you, dearest dearest … But you spoil me into an excess of liberty by your tenderness. Best in the world! Oh, you help me to live! I am better and lighter since I have drawn near to you even on this paper… —Elizabeth Barrett Browning

I love you ever and ever and without reserve. The more I have known you the more have I lov'd. In every way – even my jealousies have been agonies of Love, in the hottest fit I ever had I would have died for you. —John Keats

Latin Phrases
Eris semper in corde meo (You will always be in my heart)
Es semper in corde meo (You are always in my heart)
Semper Fidelis (Always faithful)
In perpetuum et unum diem (Forever and a day)
Amor meus amplior quam verba est (My love is more than words)
Nunc scio quid sit amor (Now I know what love is)

181. Write a love letter using these swoon worthy lines as inspiration. It can be for someone in your life or from the perspective of a character.

Illustrated

Use the following illustrations from classic books written in the 1800s to create an all-new story.

183. *Title:* _____

_____

_____

_____

_____

_____

_____

_____

_____

_____

_____

_____

_____

_____

_____

_____

_____

184. *Title:* _____

185. *Title:* _____

_____

_____

_____

_____

_____

_____

_____

_____

_____

_____

_____

_____

_____

_____

_____

_____

_____

_____

_____

_____

_____

Traditional Prompts

Writing Challenge:

Weave in some symbolism to add depth. There is a number symbolism chart in the back.

Blurb It

The blurb below can be a jumping off point for a novel or a short story. Change the names, gender, or the situation itself. The point is to having fun writing.

The Rescue

(Sample) <u>Zoe Sparrow</u> is an <u>expert swordsperson</u> from <u>Ireland</u>, who makes her living as a <u>Hollywood stuntwoman</u>. Her life is in a holding pattern until she meets <u>Tommy</u> <u>Barker</u>, a <u>mysterious</u> man with an appetite for <u>music</u> who <u>moves in across the hall</u>.

<u>Zoe</u> instantly dislikes <u>Tommy</u> and his <u>non-stop noise</u>. But, when <u>a man breaks into Zoe's apartment</u>, <u>Tommy</u> comes to the rescue. <u>Zoe</u> begins to observe that <u>Tommy</u> is really <u>kind and clever at heart</u>.

But, the tensions at <u>Tommy's job</u> at <u>the record studio</u> distract him from noticing <u>Zoe</u>'s affections, and <u>Zoe</u> begins <u>stargazing</u> to move on. However, when the <u>self-absorbed actor, Preston Thorpe</u>, from the <u>current film she is working on</u> endangers their friendship, <u>Tommy</u> has to put it all on the line. Will they find the love they crave?

185. _____ (Protagonist Name) is a(n) _____ (Area of Skill) from _____, who makes her living as a _____ (Job). Her life is in a holding pattern until she meets _____ (Love Interest = LI), a _____ (Adjective) man with an appetite for _____ (Area of Interest) who _____ (Reason for Proximity).

_____ (Protagonist) instantly dislikes _____ (LI) and his _____ (thing that annoys her). But, when _____ (Crisis), _____ (LI) comes to the rescue. _____ begins to observe that _____ (LI) is truly _____ (Good traits of the LI).

But, the tensions at _____ at _____ distract him from noticing _____ 's affections and _____ begins _____ to move on. However, when _____ from the _____, _____ (Rival), endangers their friendship, _____ has to put it all on the line. Will they find the love they crave?

Prompt # _____ Your Title: _____

If You Were

If you were ___, who/what would you be in a romance story? Explain by telling a story, using vivid verbs and sensory images.

186. a princess/prince

187. a maid/janitor

188. an ad executive

189. a teacher/professor

190. an art student

191. a college athlete

192. a nurse

193. a librarian

194. a race car driver

195. a police officer

196. a translator

197. a bank manager

198. a flight attendant

199. an apothecary

200. a time traveler

Turn Up the Heat
Just add conflict.

1. A robbery
2. On the run from the police
3. Blackmailed
4. Accused of a crime
5. Injured
6. Attracted to the wrong person
7. Locked in
8. A blackout
9. Heat wave
10. A violent storm
11. Food shortage
12. Computer virus
13. Toxic relationship
14. Alien invasion
15. Apocalypse
16. Supernatural creatures
17. Moving cities
18. New job
19. Loss of a loved one
20. Eviction

Prompt # _____ Your Title: _____

Mixed Bag

A little mix of everything to keep it interesting.

201. A performer falls in love with an ambassador from another country, only to find out that she is hiding a dark secret.

202. A spy falls in love with the sister of someone he was sent to investigate. When things go sideways, he will need to do more than investigate.

203. The government has outlawed love because all adoration should be directed towards the government who has saved humanity from doom. But can one control love?

204. He was saved by a ship full of female pirates in strangely old clothing. When he's dropped on shore, he turns, but the ship disappeared. Had he fallen for a ghost?

205. Marrying outside your social caste is reason for banishment to the wasteland. Your characters try to cheat the system.

206. Characters in this society are given a certain number of credits each month. If you drop below the minimum in your account, you are shipped off to become a slave.

207. A perfume maker creates a fragrance that makes people fall in love. Besides the disastrous effects to some people's lives, there is something even darker afoot.

208. In a civilization bound by ancient gods, it is said that a statue would weep when the princess destined to break the curse was born. It wept the day she was born. He vowed to find her.

209. When your character's family finds the suitor who will most benefit the family, your character is sent to a "premarital preparation camp." But the camp turns out to be a brainwashing facility.

210. Every night your character dreams of the same man. In this dream world, they have the relationship she's always wanted. While watching a documentary, she sees him in the background of one of the scenes. He exists.

211. Your character has been promised a promotion after years of hard work. The day before the official announcement, the company brings in a new hire from outside the company and gives the job away. No matter what, your character will drive the newbie out—no matter how attractive, charming, and amazing that person is.

Prompt # _____ Your Title: _____

Prompt # _____ Your Title: _____

Prompt # _____ Your Title: _____

Prompt # _____ Your Title: _____

_____
_____
_____
_____
_____
_____
_____
_____
_____
_____
_____
_____
_____
_____
_____
_____
_____
_____
_____
_____
_____
_____
_____

Prompt # _____ Your Title: _____

Japanese Tanka

A Practice in Brevity

Writing Challenge:

Diversify your topics and include a Japanese tanka: about a friend, a family member, and something romantic. Then tap into some emotions: happiness, sadness, indifference, and need.

Japanese tankas are a great way to practice precise language. They are five lines long. The first line is five syllables, the second is seven, the third five, the fourth is seven, and the fifth is seven (5-7-5-7-7). Here are a few samples.

They can be romantic:

Your love, is warmth like 5
The rays of a thousand suns 7
powering each glance; 5
The heat of a raging fire 7
fueling each delicate kiss. 7

—Robin Woods

Secrets buried deep 5
Within my heart in stillness 7
Waiting endlessly 5
To capture a glimpse of you 7
Looking back at me in love. 7

—Brooke E. Wayne

A sweet surrender 5
Giving into your embrace 7
My heart full of love, 5
And my soul full of longing 7
I am whole within your arms. 7

—Brooke E. Wayne

212. About new love:

_____
_____
_____
_____
_____

213. About loss of love:

_____
_____
_____
_____
_____

214. About joy of long-term love:

_____
_____
_____
_____
_____

215. About friendship:

_____

_____

_____

_____

_____

216. About a breakup:

_____

_____

_____

_____

_____

217. Your choice:

_____

_____

_____

_____

_____

218. Your choice:

219. Your choice:

220. Your choice:

Journal

Writing Challenge:

Use this space as a traditional journal, or for a list of story ideas that were inspired by the prompts.

Reference

Reference within the Workbook

Barriers in Relationships

Emotional Barriers

Abuse in the past
Anxiety
Arguing
Arranged relationship
Bitterness
Body image issues
Communication issues
Comparison
Competition
Control
Cultural conflict
Denial
Depression
Disappointment
Dishonesty
Disloyalty
Distrust
Fear
Feelings for another person
Fighting
Grief
Grudge
Guilt
Hubris (Excessive pride)
Hypochondria
Inability to choose
Inability to forgive
Inflexibility
Influence of friends or family
Insecurity
Instability
Intimacy issues
Jealousy
Mistaken identity
Mistrust
Misunderstanding
Not self-aware
Overdependence
Overreacting often
Overthinking

Passive aggressiveness
Perfectionism
Prejudice
Rage issues
Relationship low priority
Religious conflict
Rivals
Secrets
Self-doubt
Self-sabotage
Selfishness
Separation anxiety
Stalling
Stubbornness
Taking things personally
Trust issues
Unfaithfulness
Unpopularity
Unrealistic expectations
Worried a gold digger

Fear of

Abandonment
Are they "the one"
Boredom
Change
Cheating
Commitment
Conflict
Emotional unavailability
Failure
Finances
FOMO (Fear of Missing Out)
Friend Zone
Health crisis
Losing love
Losing oneself
Rejection
Repeating the past
Settling
Success

Physical Barriers

Against the rules
Age difference
Biological clock
Biological requirements
Can't be touched
Chemical Dependency
Coma
Death
Different planes of existence
Different species
Different value system
Disapproving parents
Disease
Disfigurement
Employment restrictions
Geographical distance
Illness
Imposter
Injury
Insanity
Kidnapping
Prison
Psychological Issues
Racial differences
Social status
Time difference (day or year)
Transformation

Other

Words to Use in a Romance

Strong verbs and adjectives are the key to stellar writing. Use these for inspiration.

Ached	Claimed	Dipped	Flexed	Hoarse
Acted	Clasp	Dragged	Flooded	Hot
Addicted	Clenched	Drink	Fluttered	Hug
Alive	Clever	Drive	Flung	Hungry
Alluring	Cling	Drown	Flushed	Immerse
Amazed	Clutch	Eager	Frantic	Impaled
Amorous	Coax	Eased	Frenzied	Impossible
Anguished	Coiled	Ecstasy	Friction	Incited
Arched	Come apart	Edged	Fulfilled	Inflamed
Arduous	Command	Elated	Furious	Inhaled
Assaulted	Consumed	Electric	Fuse	Insane
Awaken	Convulsed	Embraced	Galvanized	Insistent
Backed	Coursed	Enchanted	Gasped	Instinct
Bare	Covered	Encircled	Gazed	Intense
Beauty	Cradled	Enclosed	Generous	Intimate
Begged	Crashed	Encountered	Gentle	Intoxicating
Belly	Craved	Encouraged	Glorious	Invaded
Bite	Creamy	Enfolded	Goddess	Invited
Blinding	Cried	Entwined	Goose flesh	Irrepressible
Bliss	Crushed	Escalated	Gorgeous	Irresistible
Blood	Cuddled	Euphoria	Grabbed	Irrevocable
Blunt	Cupped	Exalted	Graced	Jerk
Bold	Curled	Exploded	Grasped	Joined
Bond	Curved	Explored	Gratification	Jolted
Braced	Dangerous	Exposed	Grazed	Joy
Breathe	Daring	Exquisite	Greedy	Juicy
Breathtaking	Darting	Fascinated	Gripped	Kiss
Brilliant	Deep	Feasted	Groaned	Kneel
Broken	Deft	Fed	Growled	Languorous
Brushed	Delicate	Feral	Guttural	Lean
Brutal	Delicious	Fervent	Hard	Lick
Bucked	Delirious	Fevered	Hauled	Lift
Burned	Delved	Fierce	Heady	Lips
Buried	Demanded	Fiery	Heartbreaking	Lithe
Captured	Desired	Filled	Heated	Longing
Careful	Desperate	Firm	Heaved	Lovely
Caressed	Determined	Flared	Heavy	Lover
Carnal	Devastated	Flavored	Held	Lower
Charmed	Devoured	Flesh	Hesitant	Lunge
Choked	Devout	Flew apart	Hissed	Luscious

Lush	Pressed	Scooped	Stared	Tormented
Luxurious	Primal	Scorching	Starved	Tortured
Madness	Provoked	Scoundrel	Stimulated	Touched
Magnificent	Pulled	Scraped	Stirred	Tousled
Massage	Pulsed	Scratch	Stole	Toyed
Meaningful	Pure	Scream	Stormy	Traced
Melt	Pushed	Searing	Strained	Trailed
Merciless	Quivered	Seduced	Strength	Transfixed
Mess	Racked	Sensation	Stretched	Transported
Moan	Radiant	Sensual	Stroked	Traveled
Molten	Raged	Shake	Strong	Treasured
Mouth	Raked	Shameless	Struggled	Trembled
Move	Rapid	Shapely	Stunned	Trusted
Murmur	Rapture	Shattered	Succulent	Tugged
Nails	Rasped	Shivered	Succumbed	Tumbled
Naked	Ravenous	Shock	Suggestive	Twisted
Nape	Ravished	Shouldered	Sultry	Unbidden
Navel	Raw	Shoved	Sumptuous	Undone
Need	Recklessly	Shuddered	Supple	Undulated
Nerves	Redden	Shy	Surged	Uninhibited
Nibbled	Relaxed	Sighed	Surrender	Unguarded
Nipped	Relished	Silky	Sweep	Unrelenting
Nude	Responsive	Sincere	Sweet	Untamed
Nuzzled	Restrained	Sinful	Swelled	Urged
Obsessive	Revealed	Skilled	Swift	Violent
Offered	Reveled	Skimmed	Swirled	Volatile
Opened	Reverent	Skyrocket	Tang	Voluptuous
Overwhelmed	Rich	Slammed	Tangled	Vulnerable
Panted	Ripe	Slid	Tart	Wasted
Passion	Rise	Slipped	Tasted	Weakened
Patient	Roar	Smoldering	Taut	Welcomed
Peaked	Rolled	Smoothed	Teased	Whimpered
Persistent	Rosy	Snuggled	Tempestuous	Whispered
Persuasive	Rough	Sobbed	Tempted	Wicked
Pinched	Roused	Soothed	Tentative	Wiggled
Playful	Rub	Sought	Texture	Willed
Plea	Rumbled	Soul	Thick	Wondered
Pleasure	Rushed	Sparked	Thrash	Worshiped
Pliant	Sank	Spent	Thrilled	Wrapped
Plump	Sated	Spice	Throbbed	Writhed
Plunder	Satisfaction	Spread	Tickled	Wriggled
Plunged	Savage	Squeezed	Tightened	Yanked
Potent	Savored	Squirmed	Tilted	Yearned
Powerful	Scent	Staggered	Tingled	Yielded

Character Appearance Charts

Eye Color	Blue	Sky Blue	Baby Blue	Electric Blue	Cornflower
	Brown	Chestnut	Chocolate	Cognac	Amber
	Green	Sea Green	Moss Green	Jade	Emerald
	Grey	Silver	Gunmetal Grey	Charcoal	Black
	Hazel	Russet	Nut	Honey	Yellow
	Lavender	Other:			
Eye Shape	Almond	Round	Drooping	Hooded	Close-Set
	Wide-Set	Deep-Set	Protruding	Sleepy	Squinting
	Down-Turned	Other:			
Skin Tone	Fair	Ivory	Porcelain	Milky	Snow
	Ruddy	Rose	Peach	Ochre	Golden
	Olive	Khaki	Toffee	Honey	Tawny
	Dark	Ebony	Sepia	Russet	Mahogany
	Other:				
Body Shape	Triangle	Rectangle	Hourglass	Rounded	Diamond
	Inverted Triangle	Barrel	Willowy	Husky	Wiry
	Other:				
Facial Shapes	Oval	Rectangle	Square	Heart	Oblong
	Egg	Diamond	Triangle	Narrow	Block-Like
	Other:				
Hair Color	Black	Dark Brown	Medium Brown	Ash Brown	Golden Brown
	Red	Auburn	Copper	Strawberry	Cinnamon
	Blond	Platinum	White	Silver	Grey
	Other:				

Notes:

Words for Sounds (a.k.a. Onomatopoeia)

Add appeal to your writing by making a splash with descriptive sound words.

Ahem	Clatter	Grind	Pound	Splash	Tweet
Baa	Click	Groan	Pow	Splat	Vroom
Babble	Clink	Gulp	Pulsing	Splinter	Wail
Bang	Clomp	Gurgle	Purr	Sputter	Wallop
Bark	Clonk	Guzzle	Quack	Squawk	Whack
Beat	Clop	Hammer	Racket	Squeak	Wheeze
Beep	Cluck	Hiss	Rap	Squish	Whicker
Bellow	Clunk	Hoot	Ratchet	Stomp	Whinny
Blare	Crackle	Howl	Rattle	Suck	Whip
Blast	Crash	Hubbub	Revved	Swish	Whir
Blip	Creak	Hum	Ring	Swoop	Whisper
Blop	Crinkle	Jangle	Rip	Swoosh	Whistle
Blow	Crunch	Jingle	Roar	Tap	Whiz
Boing	Din	Kerplunk	Rumble	Tatter	Woof
Bong	Ding	Knock	Rushing	Tee-Hee	Woot
Boo	Discord	Lash	Rustle	Throb	Yap
Boom	Drip	Mew	Scream	Thud	Yawp
Bop	Drone	Mewl	Screech	Thump	Yelp
Bray	Drum	Murmur	Scuff	Thunder	Yip
Bubble	Eek	Neigh	Shriek	Thwack	Yowl
Burp	Fanfare	Oink	Shuffle	Tick	Zap
Buzz	Fizz	Ooze	Sizzle	Tinkle	Zip
Cacophony	Fizzle	Patter	Slam	Titter	Zoom
Cha-Ching	Flick	Peal	Slap	Tock	
Cheep	Fling	Peep	Slop	Tolling	Other:
Chime	Flop	Pew	Slurp	Toot	
Chirp	Fracas	Pitter-Patter	Smack	Trill	
Chug	Giggle	Plink	Snap	Tromp	
Clack	Glug	Plod	Snicker	Trumpet	
Clamor	Glurp	Plop	Snigger	Tsk	
Clang	Gnashing	Plunk	Snip	Tumult	
Clank	Gobble	Poof	Snort	Tut	
Clap	Grating	Pop	Spatter	Twang	

Tastes and Aromas

When you are writing, try to incorporate all four of the senses in your work. Here is a cheat sheet for tastes and smells:

Positive	Neutral	Negative	Spices	Florals (Most Fragrant)
Aromatic	Acidic	Biting	Cajun	Angel's Trumpet
Citrusy	Acrid	Bitter	Cinnamon	Flowering Plum
Comforting	Airy	Decay	Clove	Heliotrope
Crisp	Ancient	Dirty	Coriander	Honeysuckle
Delicate	Brackish	Fetid	Cumin	Jasmine
Delicious	Burnt	Foul	Dill	Lavender
Exquisite	Delicate	Funky	Pepper	Lilac
Fragrant	Feminine	Gamy	Sage	Mexican Orange
Fresh	Fermented	Harsh	Thyme	Mock Orange
Fruity	Masculine	Moldy	Basil	Rose
Full-Bodied	Floral	Musty	Barbeque	Star Magnolia
Hard	Humid	Nasty	Bay Leaf	Sweet Peas
Heady	Light	Noxious	Curry	Tuberose
Juicy	Medicinal	Old	Anise	**Household Smells**
Lemony	Medium	Pungent	Caraway Seed	
Rich	Mellow	Putrid	Cardamom	Babies
Savory	Metallic	Rancid	Cayenne	"Boy" Smell
Sharp	Mild	Rank	Cumin	Bacon
Succulent	Minty	Repulsive	Dill	BBQ
Sugary	Moist	Rotting	Fennel	Beer
Sweet	Musky	Skunky	Garlic	Books
Tangy	Nippy	Sour	Ginger	Bread
Tart	Nutty	Spoiled	Mace	Burning Wood
Tempting	Peppery	Stagnant	Marjoram	Chocolate
Warm	Perfumed	Stale	Mint	Cinnamon
Woody	Salty	Stench	Mustard	Citrus
Zesty	Woodsy	Stinking	Onion	Coconut
Zingy	Yeasty	Stuffy	Orange Peel	Coffee
			Lemon Peel	Cut Grass
Other:	Other:	Other:	Nutmeg	Dirty Laundry
			Rosemary	Fresh–Baked Cookies
			Saffron	Fresh Laundry
			Turmeric	Pine
			Vanilla	Soap

Synonyms

As you are editing, it is important to pay attention to repetition. Much of the tinkering with words will come with editing, but I love using synonym sheets to cut down on the editing later, as well as to inspire me.

Emotions

Other words for Happy

Alluring, amused, appealing, appeased, blissful, blithe, carefree, charmed, cheeky, chipper, chirpy, content, convivial, delighted, elated, electrified, ecstatic, enchanted, enthusiastic, exultant, excited, fantastic, fulfilled, glad, gleeful, glowing, gratified, idyllic, intoxicating, jolly, joyful, joyous, jovial, jubilant, light, lively, merry, mirthful, overjoyed, pleased, pleasant, radiant, sparkling, savoured, satisfied, serene, sunny, thrilled, tickled, up, upbeat, winsome, wonderful.

Other words for SAD

Aching, agitated, anguished, anxious, bleak, bothered, brooding, bugged, chagrined, cheerless, darkly, disillusioned, disappointed, disenchanted, disheartened, dismayed, distraught, dissatisfied, despondent, doleful, failed, faint, frustrated, glazed, gloomy, glowering, haunted, hopeless, languid, miserable, pained, perturbed, sour, suffering, sullen, thwarted, tormented, troubled, uneasy, unsettled, upset, vacant, vexed, wan, woeful, wounded.

Other words for Mad

Affronted, aggravated, agitated, angered, annoyed, bitter, boiling, bothered, brooding, bugged, bummed, cantankerous, chafed, chagrined, crabby, cross, disgruntled, distraught, disturbed, enflamed, enraged, exasperated, fiery, fuming, furious, frantic, galled, goaded, hacked, heated, hostile, hot, huffy, ill-tempered, incensed, indignant, inflamed, infuriated, irate, ireful, irritated, livid, maddened, malcontent, miffed, nettled, offended, peeved, piqued, provoked, raging, resentful, riled, scowling, sore, sour, stung, taut, tense, tight, troubled, upset, vexed, wrathful.

Other words for Crying

Bawling, blubbering, gushing, howling, lamenting, moaning, scream-crying, silent tears, sniffling, snivelling, sobbing, sorrowing, teary, wailing, weepy, woeful.

Commonly Used Words

Other words for ASKED

Appealed, begged, beckoned, beseeched, besieged, bid, craved, commanded, claimed, coaxed, challenged, charged, charmed, cross-examined, demanded, drilled, entreated, enchanted, grilled, implored, imposed, interrogated, invited, invoked, inquired, insisted, needled, ordered, pleaded, petitioned, picked, probed, pried, pressed, pumped, pursued, put through the wringer, put the screws down, questioned, queried, quizzed, requested, required, requisitioned, roasted, solicited, summoned, surveyed, sweated, urged, wanted, wheedled, wooed, worried, wondered.

Other words for LAUGH

Break up, burst, cackle, chortle, chuckle, crack-up, crow, giggle, grin, guffaw, hee-haw, howl, peal, quack, roar, scream, shriek, snicker, snigger, snort, split one's sides, tee-hee, titter, whoop.

Other Words for LOOK

Address, admire, attention, audit, babysit, beam, beholding, blink, bore, browse, burn, cast, check, comb, consider, contemplate, delve, detect, discover, disregard, distinguish, ensure, evil eye, examine, explore, eye, eyeball, ferret, fix, flash, forage, gander, gaze, get an eyeful, give the eye, glance, glare, glaze, glimmer, glimpse, glitter, gloat, goggle, grope, gun, have a gander, inquire, inspect, investigate, judge, keeping watch, leaf-through, leer, lock daggers on, look fixedly, look-see, marking, moon, mope, neglect, note, notice, noting, observe, ogle, once-over, peek, peep, peer, peg, peruse, poke into, scan, pout, probe, pry, quest, rake, recognize, reconnaissance, regard, regarding, renew, resemble, review, riffle, rubberneck, rummage, scan, scowl, scrutinize, search, seeing, sense, settle, shine, sift, simper, size-up, skim, slant, smile, smirk, snatch, sneer, speculative, spot, spy, squint, stare, study, sulk, supervise, surveillance, survey, sweep, take stock of, take in, trace, verify, view, viewing, watch, witness, yawp, zero in.

Other words for REPLIED

Acknowledged, answered, argued, accounted, barked, bit, be in touch, boomeranged, comeback, countered, conferred, claimed, denied, echoed, feedback, fielded the question, get back to, growled, matched, parried, reacted, reciprocated, rejoined, responded, retorted, remarked, returned, retaliated, shot back, snapped, squelched, squared, swung, vacillated.

Other words for Sat

Be seated, bear on, cover, ensconce, give feet a rest, grab a chair, have a place, have a seat, hunker, install, lie, park, perch, plop down, pose, posture, put it there, relax, remain, rest, seat, seat oneself, settle, squat, take a load off, take a place, take a seat.

Other words for Was/Were   VERB (TO BE)

Abided, acted, be alive, befell, breathed, continued, coexisted, do, endured, ensued, existed, had been, happened, inhabited, lasted, lived, moved, obtained, occurred, persisted, prevailed, remained, rested, stood, stayed, survived, subsided, subsisted, transpired.

Other words for Walk

Advance, amble, barge, bolt, bounce, bound, canter, charge, crawl, creep, dance, dash, escort, gallop, hike, hobble, hop, jog, jump, leap, limp, lope, lumber, meander, mosey, move, pad, pace march, parade, patrol, plod, prance, proceed, promenade, prowl, race, roam, rove, run, sashay, saunter, scamper, scramble, zip shuffle, skip, slink, slither, slog, sprint, stagger, step, stomp, stride, stroll, strut, stumble, swagger, thread, tiptoe, traipse, tramp, tread, trek, trip, trot, trudge, wade, wander.

Other words for Whisper

Breathed, buzz, disclosed, exhaled, expressed, fluttered, gasped, hint, hiss, hum, hushed tone, intoned, lament, low voice, moaned, mouthed, mumble, murmur, mutter, puff, purred, reflected, ruffle, rumble, rush, said low, said softly, sigh, sob, undertone, utter, voiced, wheezed.

Other words for Went

Abscond, ambled, approached, avoided, be off, beat it, bolted, bounced, bounded, bugged out, burst, carved, cleared out, crawled, crept, cruised, cut and run, danced, darted, dashed, decamped, deserted, disappeared, ducked out, escaped, evaded, exited, fared, fled, floated, flew, flew the coop, galloped, got away, got going, got lost, glided, go down, go south, hightailed, hit the road, hoofed it, hopped, hotfooted, hurdled, hustled, journeyed, jumped, leapt, left, lighted out, loped, lunged, made haste, made a break for it, made for, made off, made tracks, marched, moseyed, moved, muscled, neared, negotiated, paced, paraded, passed, pedalled, proceeded, progressed, pulled out, pulled, pushed off, pushed on, quitted, retired, retreated, rode, ran along, ran away, rushed, sashayed, scampered, scooted, scrammed, scurried, scuttled, set off, set out, shot, shouldered, shoved off, shuffled, skedaddled, skipped out, skipped, skirted, slinked, slipped, soared, split, sprang, sprinted, stole away, steered clear, stepped on it, strolled, strutted, scurried, swept, took a hike, took a powder, took flight, took leave, took off, threaded, toddled, tottered, trampled, travelled, traversed, trekked, trode, trudged, tumbled, vamoosed, vanished, vaulted, veered, walked off, wandered, weaved, wended, whisked, withdrew, wormed, zipped, zoomed.

Other words for SAID

Accused, acknowledged, added, announced, addressed, admitted, advised, affirmed, agreed, asked, avowed, asserted, answered, apologized, argued, assured, approved, articulated, alleged, attested, barked, bet, bellowed, babbled, begged, bragged, began, bawled, bleated, blurted, boomed, broke in, bugged, boasted, bubbled, beamed, burst out, believed, brought out, confided, crowed, coughed, cried, congratulated, complained, conceded, chorused, concluded, confessed, chatted, convinced, chattered, cheered, chided, chimed in, clucked, coaxed, commanded, cautioned, continued, commented, called, croaked, chuckled, claimed, choked, chortled, corrected, communicated, claimed, contended, criticized, construe,

dared, decided, disagreed, described, disclosed, drawled, denied, declared, demanded, divulged, doubted, denied, disputed, dictated, echoed, ended, exclaimed, explained, expressed, enunciated, expounded, emphasized, formulated, fretted, finished, gulped, gurgled, gasped, grumbled, groaned, guessed, gibed, giggled, greeted, growled, grunted, hinted, hissed, hollered, hypothesized, inquired, imitated, implied, insisted, interjected, interrupted, intoned, informed, interpreted, illustrated, insinuated, jeered, jested, joked, justified, lied, laughed, lisped, maintained, muttered, marveled, moaned, mimicked, mumble, modulated, murmured, mused, mentioned, mouthed, nagged, noted, nodded, noticed,

objected, observed, offered, ordered, owned up, piped, pointed out, panted, pondered, praised, prayed, puzzled, proclaimed, promised, proposed, protested, purred, pled, pleaded, put in, prevailed, parried, pressed, put forward, pronounced, pointed out, prescribed, popped off, persisted, protested, questioned, quavered, quipped, quoted, queried, rejected, reasoned, ranted, reassured, reminded, responded, recalled, returned, requested, roared, related, remarked, replied, reported, revealed, rebutted, retorted, repeated, reckoned, remembered, regarded, recited, resolved, reflected, ripped, rectified, reaffirmed,

snickered, sniffed, smirked, snapped, snarled, shot, sneered, sneezed, started, stated, stormed, sobbed, stuttered, suggested, surmised, sassed, sputtered, sniffled, snorted, spoke, stammered, squeaked, sassed, scoffed, scolded, screamed, shouted, sighed, smiled, sang, shrieked, shrilled, speculated, supposed, settled, solved, shot back, swore, stressed, spilled, told, tested, trilled, taunted, teased, tempted, theorized, threatened, tore, uttered, unveiled, urged, upheld, vocalized, voiced, vindicated, volunteered, vowed, vented, verbalized, warned, wailed, went on, wept, whimpered, whined, wondered, whispered, worried, warranted, yawned, yakked.

My Synonym Lists:

Books by Robin Woods

Fiction

Allure: A Watcher Series Prequel

The Unintended: The Watcher Series Book One

The Nexus: The Watcher Series Book Two

The Sacrifice: The Watcher Series Book Three

The Fallen: Part One: Watcher Series Book Four

The Fallen: Part Two: Watcher Series Book Five

Non-Fiction

Prompt Me Workbook & Journal

Prompt Me Again Workbook & Journal

Prompt Me More Workbook & Journal

Prompt Me Sci-Fi & Fantasy Workbook & Journal

Prompt Me Romance Workbook & Journal

Prompt Me Novel Fiction Writing Workbook & Journal

Prompt Me Horror & Thriller Workbook & Journal

Prompt Me Reading: Literary Analysis & Journal

Picture This: Photo Prompts & Inspiration is a digital spinoff of the *Prompt Me Series* available on Kindle.

Coming in 2020: *Prompt Me Mystery & Suspense* and *Light & Shadow: The Watcher Series Shorts & Extras*

Dive into a genre and empower your creativity.

Prompt Me Horror & Thriller

All new photos and prompts

New activities

Prompt Me Sci-Fi & Fantasy

More master lists

More inspiration

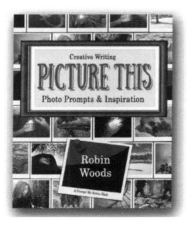

Picture This: Photo Prompts & Inspiration

Meet *Prompt Me's* Digital Cousin
52 Full Color Photo Prompts
92 Written Prompts with 422 combinations
14 Master Lists
Tip, Tricks, and Challenges

Great for writers on the go!

170 | Robin Woods

About the Author

Robin Woods currently lives in a small town on the Oregon Coast with her two kids and ever-patient husband.

She spent most of her life in California's famed Silicon Valley where she earned a BA in English and an MA in Education. In addition to writing, she taught high school English, literature, and writing for two and a half decades and worked as an university instructor.

Ms. Woods has published six highly-rated novels and has multiple projects in the works, including writing for a Hollywood producer.

For more information and free resources, go to her website at:

www.RobinWoodsFiction.com

Thank you for reading. If you enjoyed this book, please take a moment to write a review. It is the best way to help the authors you love. Books without reviews simply don't sell and your support is critical. Reviews don't have to be long. Something as simple as:

I liked ___ and ___. I would recommend it to ___.

Thank you so much. Blessings!

Made in the USA
Columbia, SC
28 November 2023

27120593R00093